Happy With Me

سعيد بذاتي

By Marisa J. Taylor

Illustrated by Vanessa Balleza

BILINGUAL

English - Arabic

I love the color of my skin. I am unique and beautiful within.

أحب لون بشرتي. أنا مميز وجميل من داخلي .

I take pride in who I am and what I can do.

أشعر بالفخر بما أنا عليه وما أستطيع أن أفعله .

Being me makes me happy from within.

كوني أنا يجعلني سعيداً من داخلي

I love to sing, dance and play with my friends, but that is just me, that makes me happy.

أحب الغناء والرقص واللعب مع أصدقائي، لكن هذا هو أنا. هذا يجعلني سعيدا.

What about you? What makes you happy?

Some of my friends love to play with toys and make a lot of noise. That is okay too, because to them it brings joy.

أصدقائي يحبون اللعب بالألعاب وإحداث الكثير من الضوضاء. لابأس في ذلك لأنه يجلب لهم الفرح .

Some of my friends love to sing, dance and chat away.
That's okay, because everyone is different and special
in their own way.

بعض من أصدقائي يحبون الغناء والرقص والدردشة. هذا جيد، لأن الجميع مختلفون ومتميزون بطريقتهم الخاصة.

I do my best to be the best version of me.

أبذل قصارى جهدي لأكون أفضل مما انا عليه .

I do not compare myself to the other children
I see. I am proud of who I am and free to be me.

لا أقارن نفسي بالأطفال الآخرين الذين أراهم. أنا فخور بمن أكون وأشعر بالحرية في أن أكون أنا.

Some children will say things and make you feel sad.

بعض الأطفال يقولون أشياء ويجعلونك تشعر بالحزن.

Don´t pay attention to their words and continue to be glad.

لا تعطي قوة لكلماتهم واستمر في أن تكون سعيداً .

Let´s support one another to be the best we can be.

دعونا ندعم بعضنا البعض لنكون أفضل .

Everyone is unique in their own special way.

كل فرد فريد بطريقته الخاصة .

Be happy with who you are and what you see.

كن سعيدا بما أنت عليه وما تراه .

It doesn't matter where in the world you are from, nor the color of your skin. BE YOU and do what makes you happy from within.

لا يهم من أي مكان في العالم أنت ولا لون بشرتك. كن نفسك وافعل ما يجعلك سعيدا من داخلك.

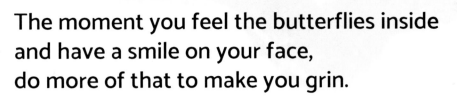

The moment you feel the butterflies inside
and have a smile on your face,
do more of that to make you grin.

في اللحظة التي تشعر فيها بالفراشات داخلك والإبتسامة مرسومة على وجهك،
افعل المزيد الذي يجعلك تبتسم.

One thing to remember
in order to be happy
from within...

شيء واحد يجب تذكره حتى
تكون سعيدًا من الداخل ...

Look at yourself in the mirror and say out loud "I am the best version of me and happy within my skin."

انظر إلى نفسك في المرآة وقل بصوت عالٍ: "أنا في افضل حالاتي وسعيد بلون بشرتي"

If you believe in and love yourself, you can achieve anything and win.

إذا كنت تؤمن بنفسك وتحبها، يمكنك تحقيق أي شيء ويمكنك أن تفوز .

Being me makes me....

كوني أنا يجعلني ....

. . . .

What about you?
What makes you happy?

وماذا عنك؟
ما الذي يجعلك سعيدا؟

LINGO
BABIES

Happy Within

سعيد بذاتي

Copyright © Lingo Babies, 2021

Written by Marisa J. Taylor

Illustrations: Vanessa Balleza

ISBN: 978-1-914605-07-9

Graphic Design: Sohail Sikandar

Translation: خلود أحمد